A Year at Sheepfold Farm

Lambing at
Sheepfold Farm

Summer at
Sheepfold Farm

Winter Comes to
Sheepfold Farm

A Year at Sheepfold Farm

Written and Illustrated by

SUSAN WILLIAMS

Piccolo Books

First published in Great Britain by Victor Gollancz Ltd in three volumes:
Lambing at Sheepfold Farm, published 1982
Summer at Sheepfold Farm, published 1983
Winter Comes to Sheepfold Farm, published 1984

This Piccolo Omnibus edition published 1986
by Pan Books Ltd, Cavaye Place, London SW10 9PG
9 8 7 6 5 4 3 2 1
Text and illustrations © Susan Williams 1982, 1983, 1984
ISBN 0 330 29468 7
Printed and bound in Great Britain
by Cox & Wyman Ltd, Reading

For my Mother

Contents

Part One

Lambing at Sheepfold Farm

page 9

Part Two

Summer at Sheepfold Farm

page 57

Part Three

Winter Comes to Sheepfold Farm

page 111

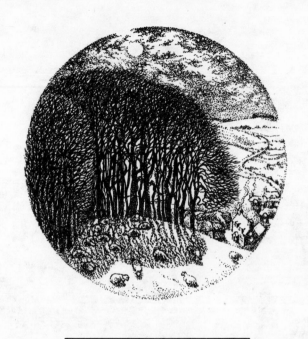

Part One

Lambing at Sheepfold Farm

This story is based on a particular lowland lambing. Lambings on other farms can be quite different. Some take place in open fields, others on moors and hillsides.

Chalkbourne village and Sheepfold Farm lie in a valley on the edge of South Wiltshire downland, although you will not find them on a map.

It was a still, cold February night. A bright moon sailed high above Chalkbourne Downs, its pale light flooding field and trackway and sparkling on the frosty rooftops of Sheepfold Farm.

Sheep camped in the shelter of beech clumps and hedgerows.

Beyond the farm, yellow lights glimmered in Chalkbourne Village.

In the shepherd's cottage, Jack and Betty Evans were looking at a plan of Jack's lambing site and trying to talk above the din of yaps and shrieks that filled the kitchen as Tim and Polly played tug of war with Patch, the Collie pup.

Jack was shepherd at Sheepfold Farm. Towards the end of February every year the whole family moved to a caravan and shepherd's hut at the lambing site high up on the Downs, so that Jack and Betty could keep a constant watch on the pregnant ewes and new lambs.

'It won't be long before the ewes start dropping their lambs. We'll have to move up there soon,' said Jack. He had found several new-born lambs that evening when he had checked the pregnant ewes already at the site.

'When, Dad, when can we go?' Polly shouted from under the table, where she and Tim were tussling with Patch. The scuffle increased and bodies thumped against Jack's and Betty's legs.

'In your place,' said Jack sternly to the pup.

Patch was only a few months old. Polly and Tim were looking after him at home until he was ready to begin working with Floss and Tib, Jack's older Collies.

'At last we'll have some peace and quiet,' said Betty, heaving a sigh of relief. Patch slept in his box by the kitchen stove, worn out after the game.

Polly and Tim leant over the plan of the lambing site.

'Where will you put the caravan and shepherd's hut this year, Dad?' Tim asked.

'And where will the heat lamp pen for the weak lambs be?' Polly wanted to know.

'We'll decide when the site is ready,' Jack said. He pushed back his chair, thinking about all the jobs still to be done. 'I'll go back up there for a few hours and work on a bit,' he said.

'We must move at the end of this week,' Jack announced at breakfast next morning. He had spent all night up at the lambing site, watching over several ewes as they gave birth.

On Friday evening the cottage was in a muddle. Betty packed boxes of saucepans, tins of food, warm clothes, sleeping bags and blankets. Polly and Tim emptied their bags of all the bulky jumpers and thick socks their mother had put in and stuffed them full of favourite toys and books.

'We should take the hens up to the site with us,' said Betty on Saturday morning. 'Then we'll have fresh eggs every day.'

Catching six hens and one fierce cockerel was not easy but finally the reluctant birds were put in a crate in Jack's van.

Polly found Beulah, their grey cat, hiding in a dark corner under a bed, hoping she would be left behind.

They had a squashed and bumpy ride to the lambing site.

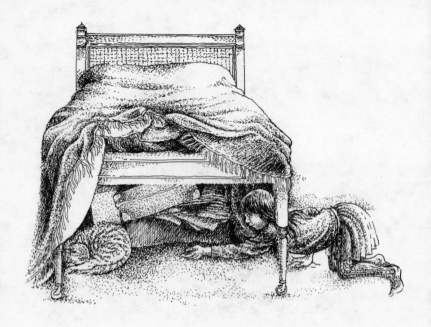

Beulah yowled and dug her claws into Tim's knees. Patch was sick on Polly's lap. The hens cackled indignantly every time the van jolted over deep ruts in the track.

Floss and Tib ran behind them.

As soon as they arrived, Jack opened the van doors and Beulah streaked out.

Polly and Tim staggered to and from the caravan with groceries and bedding, and Betty put the hens into a run.

Jack had worked hard to prepare for lambing.

In the autumn, he had divided the fifteen hundred ewes in his care into three flocks, each to lamb one after the other in the spring.

Six weeks ago Floss and Tib had helped him bring the early lambing flock to Field Barn, where they would stay until their lambs were safely born.

Part of Field Barn was taken up with two large lambing yards, and about a hundred ewes would stay in each of these until they gave birth. There were more lambing yards outside the barn for the rest of the flock.

Down the middle of the barn Jack and Walt Roberts, the tractor driver, had built small coops for each ewe and her lamb immediately after birth.

When the lambs were a day old, they were moved with their mothers to mothering pens alongside the barn. Here Jack could keep a careful eye on them for a few days, until they were strong enough to be turned out into the paddocks.

In the paddocks, Walt had tied sacking to the wire fences to make windbreaks, while Jack had built rough shelters to protect the young lambs from bad weather.

When the lambs were four or five days old, they were turned out into the open fields.

Everyone was kept busy moving the ewes and their growing lambs from one place to another.

The caravan and shepherd's hut were parked under the barn roof. Polly and Tim were to sleep in the old hut, which Jack had bought from a shepherd who had lived in it years ago at lambing time.

Betty lit a small fire in the cast iron stove that stood in the corner of the hut.

'Old Harry used to warm the orphan lambs' milk on this stove,' she said.

They carried two mattresses, sleeping bags and plenty of extra blankets into the hut. Betty made up bunk beds on two wide shelves.

'Mine's the top bunk, I'm oldest,' Tim said at bedtime.

'Oh, all right,' Polly agreed, 'but I'm having Patch sleep under my bed – can he, Mum?'

'Only for tonight. Tomorrow he must go with Floss and Tib. They've made themselves a good den under your hut,' said Betty, raking out the last glowing embers from the stove. The wood-lined hut kept warm all night long.

Deep-throated baas of ewes and shrill bleats of young lambs sounded in Tim's and Polly's ears as they fell asleep.

Early next morning Jack and Walt took a trailer-load of hay and sacks of crushed corn to feed the two flocks of pregnant ewes out in the fields.

Since December, hay made on the farm in the summer had been fed to the sheep. Now with lambing approaching, Jack and Walt were also giving the sheep crushed oats and barley to make sure they produced big healthy lambs and plenty of milk.

'This lot look well enough,' said Walt, as they walked up and down, watching the ewes eat.

'Yes, fit and full of lambs, I hope,' said Jack. 'We'd best get on and feed the others in Forty Acres.'

They filled the hay racks, checked round the field for sick ewes, and broke thick ice in the water troughs.

Walt banged his feet and rubbed his hands. 'Reckon snow's on the way,' he grumbled.

Back at Field Barn the ewes set up a hungry baaing chorus. They could hear the uproar on the hillside and knew the tractor would soon arrive with their food.

Polly fetched hay from the stack in the barn and stuffed it into small racks hanging in each coop.

Tim refilled the water buckets, so that the sheep had plenty to drink.

When Jack and Walt had fed the ewes in Field Barn they went to the paddocks where there were already some lambs

with their mothers. Ewes with suckling lambs needed extra food to keep their milk supplies going until the spring grass grew.

'Look out for any ewes mooning about in corners on their own,' Betty said to Tim and Polly. The children knew the signs of lambing well. A ewe would paw the ground, snuffling the straw, and glance round at her hindquarters, making soft baaing noises. Jack always called this 'talking to her lamb'.

Before a lamb was born, the water bag which protected the lamb while it grew inside its mother appeared, hanging like a yellowish globe from the ewe's backside.

Then she would lie down away from the other sheep and begin to strain, pushing her lamb out from her body.

As the ewes gave birth, Betty, Tim and Polly picked up new-born lambs and coaxed the mothers to follow them from the lambing yards to the coops in the centre of the barn.

When each ewe was left alone with her lambs, she would lick the lambing fluids from their fleeces with her warm comforting tongue and nudge them gently to their feet. Soon they were taking their first wobbly steps, and seeking out their mother's udder for a drink of milk.

At supper that evening, Polly and Tim were feeling tired
but satisfied after the day's hard work. Then they remembered that the next day was Monday.

'Do we have to go to school tomorrow? You need us to
help here,' they said to Betty and Jack.

'Of course you must go to school,' said Betty.

'Walt thinks there's snow in the air, though,' said Jack,
trying to cheer them up.

The lambing site was a different world from school and the
village. Last year some children had turned up their noses at
the strong sheepy smell which hung about Tim and Polly's
clothes.

'I like the smell of sheep,' Polly had said to them crossly.

26

When Tim and Polly looked out of the shepherd's hut next morning, everything was white.

Ewes and lambs in the outdoor mothering pens stood with snowy layers on their backs.

Inside the barn the ewes were dry and content, blowing steamy clouds of breath into the cold morning air. Lambs nestled on the soft mounds of their mothers' backs or against their sides.

Betty was busy with the new-born lambs.

'No school today,' she said. 'The track is blocked. Your dad and Walt are having a terrible job getting through to the ewes in the fields.'

'Hooray! We're snowed up for weeks and weeks,' shouted

Polly.

Hours went by before they saw the tractor returning through the deep snow. They ran to help unload a sick ewe which Walt and Jack had brought back.

Walt handed Betty two lambs. 'Found 'em when we checked round the paddocks,' he said. 'Plenty of shelter, but these little 'uns must've lost their mums and gone without a drink last night.'

Betty hurried away to put the starved lambs under a heat lamp. When they had revived in the warmth, she fed them ewe's milk from a bottle.

'Dad!' called Tim from one of the lambing yards.

'What's the trouble?' asked Jack, coming over to where Tim stood watching two ewes circling a couple of lambs, licking them eagerly in turn.

'Which lamb belongs to which mother?' asked Tim.

'She hasn't lambed yet,' Jack said, looking at them carefully and pointing to the smaller ewe. 'She's a pincher. She'll lamb soon and reject her own because she's already taken to these two. Give me a hand to put the real mother into a pen with her twins. Daft stubborn things, ewes can be.'

The snow fell steadily all day.

'We're running out of coops. We'll have to turn some ewes and lambs out into the most sheltered mothering pens,' said Jack. He and Walt set to work choosing big, well-fed lambs born the night before. They sprayed a number on each ewe and her lambs so that they could be paired up easily if they were separated. Then they put thick rubber rings on the lambs' tails to make them wither and drop off in a few weeks' time. When the warmer weather came, lambs with short tails would be much cleaner and less bothered by flies.

Betty, Polly and Tim opened the gates at the front of the coops and each picked up a lamb. They walked slowly to the mothering pen entrance, showing the lambs to their mothers.

The lambs bawled loudly when they were set down in the cold unfamiliar whiteness of the mothering pen, and their mothers rushed up to them, baaing anxiously. They recog-

nised their own lambs by sniffing them as they suckled, and
would butt strange lambs away if their smell was unfamiliar.
Polly secretly thought the ewes could read the lambs'
numbers!

Long after Polly and Tim were asleep in the shepherd's hut, Jack patrolled the floodlit lambing site with a torch to shine into shadowy corners where a ewe might be having a difficult lambing.

Sometimes a lamb was born completely encased in its water bag. Jack would quickly break the bag and clear the lamb's nose and mouth so that it could breathe.

Towards midnight the snow stopped falling and the water in the troughs began to freeze.

Floss, Tib and Patch burrowed deeply into their den of straw under the shepherd's hut, and dreamed sheepy dreams.

Beulah crept among the warm heap of lambs under the heat lamp.

The hens roosted with fluffed-out feathers inside their snowed-up hen hut.

'Polly. *Polly*!'

Tim's voice floated into Polly's dream about digging sheep out of snowdrifts.

'Wake up! It's stopped snowing and the sun's out!'

After breakfast Polly and Tim took their toboggan to a steep slope along the hillside track leading to the farm. There was now a smooth glistening path through the drifts, where the tractor had flattened the snow.

Patch bounded ahead, diving into dark corners and sniffing at the animal tracks criss-crossing the path in front of him.

'We'll race you down the hill, Patch,' said Polly, as Tim gave the toboggan a push. Faster and faster they hurtled down the track, with snow flying in their eyes. In another minute they had crashed into a deep drift.

Patch's faint yap came through the blanket of snow.

Polly sat up and cupped her hands round her mouth: 'PATCH! COME HERE!' she yelled.

Patch barked again from the other side of the hedge, and Polly and Tim heard a low bleat. They climbed over a gate into the field.

Patch was crouching a little way off from the humps and bumps of the hedgerow drift. As they drew nearer they saw that one of the humps was a snow-covered ewe.

Polly knelt down and scooped the snow away from the ewe. 'Here's a tiny lamb,' she said.

'It's early, this flock isn't supposed to start lambing until next week,' said Tim.

There were some more sharp yaps from Patch. He was running across the field, past the other ewes browsing through piles of hay scattered over the snow.

As Polly and Tim ran after him, they noticed a line of dog-like prints spattered with a thin trail of blood.

Patch stopped by a hollow in the snow. A frail blood-stained lamb opened its mouth stiffly and let out a long wailing bleat.

'A fox has had it,' said Tim. He and Polly had seen lambs attacked by foxes before. 'We'd better get them back to Field Barn.'

Polly picked up the lambs and showed them to their mother. With Tim's help the ewe heaved herself up from the drift, baaing softly. Once out on the track, Polly sat on the toboggan, cradling the lambs closely to her, while Tim hauled slowly uphill. Patch plodded along behind the ewe.

'A medal for the shepherd and shepherdess,' said Jack, when at last they reached Field Barn.

'Not forgetting the sheep dog,' Tim said proudly.

'I can't think how Walt and I missed that ewe this morning at feeding,' said Jack, as he fixed a heat lamp over the pen for the exhausted ewe and her lambs. 'It looks as though she had quite a fight with the fox.'

Polly ran to fetch a small plastic tube with a length of rubber pipe attached to one end. Betty used this for feeding lambs when they were too weak to suckle from their mothers or a bottle.

'Quickly, Polly,' said Betty. She squeezed some milk from the ewe's udder into a jug.

Polly held the weakest lamb's head steady, as her mother slipped the thin rubber pipe down its throat and into its stomach. Then Polly carefully poured a little of the ewe's milk into the tube, adding a few drops of warm glucose.

When the milk had drained away into the pipe, Betty swiftly withdrew it. They repeated the treatment with the other lamb.

Jack examined the weaker lamb and found it was not as badly injured as they had thought. As a reward for their part in the rescue – and because the ewe had very little milk – Jack gave it to Polly and Tim.

'We'll call her Crystal – *if* she lives,' said Polly, 'and her brother Snowy and her mum – '

'Foxfighter,' said Tim.

By evening Snowy was suckling vigorously from Foxfighter, and Crystal had revived enough to suck milk from a bottle.

After the snow rescue there was one week of tobogganing and snowball fights before a thaw set in and Polly and Tim had to go back to school.

Floss and Tib helped drive the second flock of ewes to the barn to lamb. The first flock had finished now and were out in the fields.

It was wild March weather and Jack and Walt often brought in lambs covered with mud and chilled to the bone. Polly and Tim rubbed them dry with soft hay and fed them warm milk.

Sometimes the lambs were found too late, stretched out stiffly in a corner of a field, their eyes pecked out by crows.

'It's the blackthorn winter,' said Walt one raw sunny morning at the end of March. 'Spring's not far off now.'

Sure enough, spiky blackthorn trees along the hedgerows were showing their delicate white blossom, and wild violets and celandine bloomed on sheltered banks.

During the Easter holidays lots of people came up to the lambing site to buy a pet lamb, and Jack would let them have an orphan. He often took a lamb away from a ewe with triplets because she did not have enough milk to feed them all. Sometimes these lambs were looked after by other ewes, but if Jack could not find a mother to take them, they were reared on the bottle and put in the orphan pen.

Polly's special favourite was a tiny lamb called Spindly. At first Betty fed him with the tube, but as he grew stronger Polly took over and bottle-fed him. She was very fond of him.

One day Spindly would not suck at his bottle. He stood listlessly in a corner of the orphan pen. Jack gave him a penicillin injection.

'We'll put him under the heat lamp for a bit,' said Betty. 'He's probably got a chill.'

As soon as she was dressed next morning Polly ran to give him his breakfast feed. All the other lambs were snuggled up together, but Polly could not see Spindly.

'They've *sold* him!' she thought, and rushed back to the caravan to find Jack or Betty.

Betty put her arms round Polly, who was sobbing angrily.

'I'm afraid I found Spindly dead this morning,' she said gently.

A few days after Spindly's death Jack said to Polly, 'Come and help Floss and Tib walk the last flock to the barn.'

It was a crisp sunny morning, and Polly soon forgot her sadness as she and Tim and the dogs kept the pregnant ewes at a steady trot towards Field Barn.

'There'll be trouble with this bunch,' said Walt. The flock included about a hundred ewe lambs, young sheep barely a year old. They often had diffiuclty giving birth because they were not yet fully grown. Sometimes they dropped their lambs and ran off, refusing to have anything to do with them.

That afternoon, Jack had his eye on a black-faced ewe

44

lamb who was straining in one of the yards.

'She's been like that for too long,' he said to Polly and Tim. 'Bring the lambing cream and let's have a look at her.'

The ewe lamb jumped up as Jack and the children approached, her eyes full of wild fear. Swiftly, Jack caught her round the neck with his crook and laid her on the straw bedding of the yard. He put on a thin plastic glove and, covering it with lambing cream, very carefully slipped his hand into the ewe lamb's birth canal.

'Why can't she get it out, Dad?' asked Tim, stroking the ewe lamb's face and holding her down.

'The lamb's front legs are bent back under its body,' said Jack. Gradually he eased one leg, then the other, into the normal position, and pulled gently. 'Now we're all right,' he said as the head and shoulders followed.

With a watery whoosh a black lamb slithered onto the straw. It sneezed the fluid out of its nostrils and shook its head.

Jack prodded the ewe lamb's belly gently. 'She's got another lamb coming,' he said. He felt inside the ewe lamb again and produced two back legs. 'Only just in time.' He quickly pulled out a much smaller black lamb. It lay limply on the straw, not breathing.

'Is it dead?' asked Polly.

Jack slapped its ribs and breathed into its mouth. Then he picked it up by its back legs and swung it to and fro. The lamb spluttered feebly and filled its lungs with air.

The mother was on her feet now, licking her first lamb cautiously.

'Let's move her into a coop with them before she runs off,' said Jack.

'Dad, could we have the little black lamb?' asked Polly. She knew that a ewe lamb would not have enough milk to feed twins.

'Please, Dad, Crystal needs a playmate. She misses Spindly a lot,' added Tim.

'First of all you'd better make sure it's going to live by asking your mum to give it a tube feed,' said Jack.

Little Blackie spent a few days under the heat lamp before she was strong enough to go in the orphan pen.

She soon learnt from Crystal when their mealtimes were. They would slip out of the pen and beat on the door of the caravan with their hard little hooves, baaing loudly.

———

Polly and Tim were up early on Easter Sunday. They prowled about the barn, looking for the glimmer of foil-wrapped chocolate eggs hidden in the hay.

Polly was startled by an angry hen she disturbed on a clutch of real eggs. Now it was spring, the hens had taken to wandering into the barn, pecking at stray corn husks and nesting in quiet corners.

Tim pounced on some chocolate eggs, half hidden in Foxfighter's hay rack. Bits of silver paper stuck out of her mouth as she munched.

'How many eggs have you eaten, you cheeky sheep?' Tim asked her.

Out in the fields, the lambs began to graze the rich spring grass and grew rapidly. They would stay with their mothers until they were big enough to make good lamb chops. Polly and Tim didn't like to think of that when they watched the lambs racing and gambolling together in the sun.

'We're not eating Blackie or Crystal,' Polly declared. 'They're going to grow up to have lambs of their own.'

'It's time we were off home,' said Jack one warm stuffy afternoon in the barn. There were only twenty ewes left in the lambing yards.

'We could turn these last few into a paddock, it would be much healthier for them,' said Betty.

On the day they were due to leave, Polly and Tim were playing in the barn. Suddenly Polly gave a shout: 'Look! Beulah's here. She's had kittens!'

There was Beulah, tucked into a hole in the haystack, her body curved round four mewling scraps of fur.

'Please can Blackie and Crystal come with us now? Patch is big enough to run behind with Floss and Tib,' Polly begged her father, who was cramming bags and boxes into the van.

'And I'll have Beulah and the kittens on my lap in Mum's old shopping basket,' offered Tim.

They peered out the dusty back windows of the van as it rattled down the track to Sheepfold Farm.

'There's Foxfighter and Snowy coming to the fence to say goodbye,' said Polly, sad, in a way, to be going home.

When they got to the cottage, children, lambs, cat and kittens spilled out of the van. Betty unlocked the front door and Polly shooed Crystal and Blackie into the garden.

Patch lolloped about in the kitchen knocking things over and getting hissed at by Beulah, who still lay in the shopping basket guarding her kittens.

They sat down to tea, surrounded by all their unpacked boxes.

'It's been the best lambing ever,' said Tim.

'Not quite over yet,' Jack reminded him. 'There are still those twenty ewes to lamb, and I'll be checking round all the ewes and lambs twice a day. Now that the warm weather's come, and the ewes are itchy in their thick winter fleeces, we'll have to watch out for them rolling onto their backs.'

Polly and Tim had been with Jack when he'd found ewes stuck on their backs with their bellies full of gases, and knew they died if they were not turned over.

'After shearing you won't have that worry,' Betty said. 'Then we'll have a holiday.'

There was a loud baaing outside. Polly opened the door a crack.

'All right, you two, we're coming with your milk in a minute,' she said to Blackie and Crystal, laughing at them.

The lambs settled down on the doorstep to wait for their supper, with Floss and Tib sprawled beside them.

Part two

Summer at Sheepfold Farm

Tim Evans lay on a footbridge over the Chalkbourne stream, peering into the fast flowing water. A big brown trout lurked somewhere in the shadows under the bridge. Tim had been trying to catch it for days.

The sound of a cuckoo echoed in a distant wood and bees hummed in the sweet-smelling May blossom overhanging the stream.

Up on the Downs, the Sheepfold Farm ewes called to their half grown lambs.

As Tim walked home along the lane to the village with only two small trout in his bag, the shepherd's van screeched to a halt beside him.

Lambing had finished over a month ago, but Jack Evans, the shepherd at Sheepfold Farm, still needed to check the ewes and lambs twice a day until shearing. His children, Polly and Tim, often went with him. They enjoyed bumping round the summer pastures in the van.

Tim climbed into the back with Polly and the three bouncing collies, Floss, Tib and Patch, and they set off, zigzagging across the fields.

'Hello, here's trouble,' said Jack, slowing down by a lamb which was shaking its tail and biting at its back leg. He stopped the van and let Floss and Tib out with Polly and Tim. Patch was still rather too young and wild to separate lambs from the flock.

'Walk up!' Jack commanded. The two collies crept forward, moving a little group of ewes and lambs into a corner against the hedge.

63

'Hold 'em up!' called Jack and he darted into the middle, catching the lamb with his crook. He examined the place that it had been trying to bite. 'Fly strike,' he said to Polly and Tim. 'Bring me my hand shears and the can of fly dip from the van.'

They watched him clip away the dirty wool from the lamb's hindquarters and saw a mass of yellow, wriggling maggots burrowing into its skin. In warm weather, flies often laid their eggs in the fleeces of ewes and lambs. The eggs hatched out into maggots which would eat the animal alive if they were not noticed.

Jack splashed some of the disinfectant dip solution over the maggots, which immediately curled up and dropped away from the lamb's skin.

'Look Dad! Isn't that Lop Ear on her back?' Polly pointed to a hollow in the field. Their favourite old ewe lay kicking her legs in the air.

'This warm weather makes them itchy. I'll be glad when all the ewes are shorn,' said Jack as they approached her.

When a sheep rolled over to scratch her back she often could not get on to her feet without help, especially if she was on uneven ground.

They heaved Lop Ear up and steadied her to make sure she did not keel over again. Her sides were distended with gases from the grass fermenting in her stomach. While she lay on her back, the ewe could not get rid of these gases.

'Another hour and she would have been dead, with a belly as tight as a drum,' said Jack.

They ate Tim's trout, lightly grilled, for supper that evening. Beulah the grey cat and her four kittens purred loudly under the kitchen table, hoping for scraps.

'There was a message from the farm tonight. The shearers are coming next Monday, for three days,' said Betty Evans.

'Oh good, it's half term. We can help, can't we, Mum?' said Polly. 'And how about doing some night fishing?' she whispered to Tim. 'We might catch your crafty old trout.'

'Hmm, I'm not sure about that,' said Jack, overhearing. 'You don't want to be mistaken for poachers.'

'That reminds me,' said Betty. 'Mrs White at the village shop was saying that sheep rustlers are about again. Watkins' shepherd had twenty taken the other day.'

Jack looked worried. 'I'll have to check round later in the evening.' He sighed. 'Just as things were getting a bit easier after lambing.'

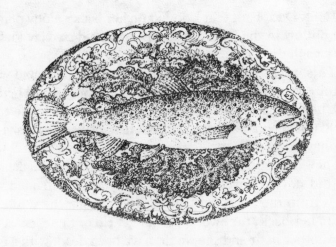

At four o'clock next Monday morning, the villagers of Chalkbourne were woken by an uproar of baaing, mixed with barks and whistles, which drifted down from the hillside.

Jack and Walt Roberts, the tractor driver, watched the dogs gathering the first three hundred sheep to be shorn.

'They're shifting 'em quick,' said Walt to Jack.

'Yes,' said Jack, 'it's much better to move sheep in the cool of the morning. We're going to have a hot day.'

'And by the time we get 'em to Field Barn the ewes will have shaken the dew from their fleeces, so they'll be dry enough for shearing,' said Walt.

When Betty, Polly and Tim arrived at Field Barn, Jack and Walt were already running the first flock of sheep through a drafting gate, to separate the lambs from the ewes. Two more tractor drivers and two women from the village had come to help.

'Come on there, Polly and Tim,' shouted Walt above the din of baas and bleats. 'Help push these ewes through to the shearing pens – else we'll never get started.'

Polly and Tim hullooed loudly and banged the sides of the metal barriers that formed a corridor leading to the drafting gate. From here, the two tractor drivers, Bob White and Bert Penny, packed the ewes into a series of pens behind the shearing platform. Their bewildered lambs ran out of the barn to the yard, baaing for their mothers.

All was now ready for the shearers. The exhausted dogs lay stretched out in the shade, with one eye still on the sheep.

At seven o'clock, the shearer's van drove up the track and four men got out.

Every June, a gang of shearers came to shear the fifteen hundred ewes in the Sheepfold Farm flock. There were usually a few Australians or New Zealanders in the gang, who had come to England for the shearing season. They were

experts and some could shear a ewe in about a minute. Each man was paid fifty pence a ewe; he kept a record of the number he had completed on a 'tally watch' that hung from his shearing machine.

'You've brought good weather with you,' said Jack, as he helped to assemble the shearing platform, and the metal frame on which the shearers hung their machines.

'We need it, mate. Last week's wet weather really held us up,' said Yorky, an Australian who came every year to Sheepfold Farm.

The shearers fitted their newly sharpened combs and cutters to their shearing hand-pieces, and oiled them well. The combs and cutters would need to be changed often during the day to ensure clean, fast shearing.

Polly borrowed Yorky's hat and swaggered about the barn like a cowboy.

Very soon, the air was filled with the whirring noise of shearing machines as the men set to work on their first sheep.

To begin with, the fleece was opened up – rather like unzipping an anorak, Polly thought – by a long cut from breast to belly.

Each shearer held his sheep firmly and, skilfully turning her first to one side, then the other, he peeled the wool away from her body.

The creamy white inside of the fleece rippled down on to the boards around each ewe until, with a skip of surprise at her new slender self, she ran free, out into the yard to find her lambs.

As soon as the whole fleece fell to the floor, one of the helpers scooped it up and flung it, outside uppermost, on to tarpaulins laid out next to the shearing platform.

Then they folded the long edges inwards to the middle and rolled up the fleece firmly. They left some wool at the neck end which they twisted and pulled into a strong rope, wound tightly round the bundle and tucked into itself.

Polly and Tim tossed the rolled fleeces into big woolsacks and jumped on them to press them well down. Soon their hands, arms and legs were sticky with the lanolin from the sheep's wool. When each sack was full, Walt came over and sewed it up with a large needle and special twine.

The gang worked steadily all morning, allowing themselves a few breaks for cooling drinks. The unshorn ewes panted beneath their thick fleeces.

'Won't be long now girls!' shouted Bob White, shooing them through the pens towards the shearing platform.

'This lot are good workers. The rollers and packers are having to move fast to keep up with them,' said Walt to Jack as they pulled out ewes for the shearers.

'Yorky's the fastest – he's done nearly a hundred already,' said Tim. He and Polly had been comparing numbers on the shearers' tally watches.

At last it was dinner time and everyone flopped down with relief.

Betty produced two big jugs of iced lemonade, cans of beer and sandwiches. After dinner the grown-ups had a snooze while Polly and Tim slid down the bulging wool sacks.

For the next few days, everyone was kept very busy supplying the shearers with sheep, rolling and packing the fleeces, and moving the shorn ewes and their lambs back to their pasture. On the third evening the final pen of sheep was completed.

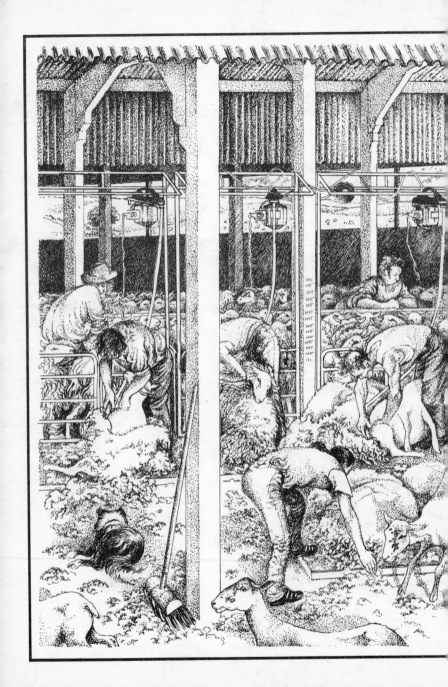

The wool sacks were stacked in the barn, ready to be loaded on to lorries which would take them to a warehouse. There the wool would be sorted and graded with fleeces from many other flocks.

The shearers put away their gear and climbed stiffly into their van. Yorky wasn't too worn out to bundle Polly into a wool sack when she stole his hat again.

'See you next year!' they called as they passed Jack and his helpers driving the last flock back to the field.

Polly, Tim and the others whooped and shouted, the dogs gathered up stragglers and the flock scampered before them, the newly shorn ewes looking like ghostly sheep in the twilight.

The hot sunny shearing weather continued and Walt began cutting the green hayfields. Everyone on the farm helped to gather in the crop and one end of Field Barn was soon filled with bales of sweet-smelling hay, which would feed the sheep in the coming winter.

Polly and Tim decided to cycle over to Blagdon Farm, to see Walt's niece Brenda Roberts, who was shepherdess there.

'We'll take Patch,' said Polly. 'Dad's not using him today and he looks bored at home.'

They swooped down the hill into the sheep yards at Blagdon, to find Brenda running some of her ewes through a foot bath. Polly, Tim and Patch helped her to push them along.

'Thanks,' she said afterwards as they sat in a shady corner of a hayfield having a picnic. 'That extra help was really handy – my dog Fly went missing a couple of weeks ago. Lovely dog he was – best worker I ever had. Shouldn't be at all surprised if the gang that pinched Watkins' sheep didn't have something to do with it.'

With haymaking over, Jack weighed some of the oldest lambs to see if any were ready to be sent for slaughter. From now until the end of the summer Jack would be sending off batches of lambs as they fattened. He would keep some of the best ewe lambs to add to the flock, but for most of them it was the end of their short lives and time for their mothers to have a good rest before the next lambing season.

Polly and Tim were helping Jack up at Field Barn when Mr Fairweather, the farmer at Sheepfold Farm, stopped by.

'How are they doing Jack?' he asked.

'Very well. I've picked out nearly a hundred over thirty-seven kilos in weight,' said Jack. Polly and Tim had been dotting these with a red mark as they came out of the weigher. Some of them were beginning to look like small sheep; quite unlike the long-legged, delicate creatures the children had cared for in the snowy weeks of March.

'We ought to send this lot as soon as possible, before we start dipping,' said Jack. Once they had been dipped, lambs could not be sold for a fortnight, in case their meat was tainted by the poisonous chemicals in the dip.

'I'll order the lorry for next Monday,' said Mr Fairweather, carefully feeling the backs and tails of some of the best lambs in the weigher to make sure they were fit enough to send.

'They have grown well, considering they're only just four months old,' he said.

When the first hundred lambs had gone to the slaughterhouse, Jack and Walt started to dip the ewes and remaining lambs. After school, Polly and Tim put on their oldest clothes and went up to the barn to help.

The dip was a long concrete pit with a sloping ramp at one end. Jack and Walt filled it with water and added a strong disinfectant to protect the sheep against fly strike, and a disease called sheep scab, caused by a tiny mite burrowing into the sheep's skin.

Sheep had to be dipped twice in the summer months. The first dipping took place about a month after shearing, once a fine layer of curly fleece had grown again on the ewes' backs.

Plenty of people were needed to chivvy the line of reluctant sheep, until one by one they leapt into the water, showering everyone with dip.

Betty stood by and dunked the ewes and lambs with a wooden dipping crook.

'They can all swim, can't they Mum?' Polly asked, watching anxiously as the sheep surfaced and paddled from one end of the dip to the other.

The whole length of the dip was filled with struggling woolly bodies, and Betty slowed them down with her crook.

By law they had to stay in for at least a minute, so that the dip solution soaked their fleeces properly.

Then they scrambled up the ramp into draining pens, their fleeces heavy with dip streaming off them.

That evening, Tim and Polly finally planned their midnight fishing expedition. Tim was determined to have another go for the big trout under the bridge.

When they were sure Betty and Jack were asleep, they crept out of a downstairs window and wheeled their bikes from the shed.

Soon they were whizzing along the dark lanes, balancing fishing rods and bait boxes across their handlebars. Pale clouds of moths flew into the beams of their bike lamps and they swerved to avoid a hedgehog ambling across the road.

'Hope he's still there,' said Tim as they leant their bikes against some trees by the bridge. There was a fiercely whispered argument about who was to have first cast and Polly stumped off round a bend to fish further upstream.

Tim baited his hook with a juicy maggot collected from a lamb with fly strike. He flicked his line into the water, allowing it to drift downstream, and waited.

It was warm, moonless night; the air was heavy with the scent of meadowsweet that grew beside the stream.

SPLASH! His rod bent with the weight of the trout, which had shot from its shelter to seize the bait. Tim reeled in the line and heard the thump of a large fish's body hitting the bank somewhere in the darkness. He searched in the long grass with his bike torch.

Tim was wrapping the silverygold trout in dock leaves when he heard Polly running back along the bank.

'Tim!' her voice was a mixture of alarm and excitement. 'I've just seen a big truck and a Land Rover go up to Marleycombe Hill. It can't be anyone from the farm at this time of night.'

They jumped on their bikes and peddled furiously up the track.

Ahead of them, long beams of light were sweeping one of the fields in which the sheep were grazing.

Amid the noise of ewes and lambs baaing, Polly and Tim heard a series of soft whistles.

The children looked at one another, their hearts thumping in their chests. Whoever was in the field was up to no good. They dumped their bikes under a bush and moved forward cautiously.

They soon saw that the beams came from the Land
Rover's headlights as it careered over the grass, pushing
some ewes and lambs towards the open back of a truck.

'Tim!' Polly clutched her brother's arm. 'Look! They're
taking Lop Ear and her lambs.' She had caught a glimpse of
the old ewe being prodded up the ramp of the truck by a
rather cruel-looking man with a face like a weasel and a gold
ring glinting in one ear. A young collie snapped at Lop Ear's
heels and Polly thought she heard the man say 'Down Fly!'
in a low voice.

'They didn't even bother to shut the gate after them,' said Tim indignantly as the Land Rover and truck roared off. He closed it himself, before any of the remaining sheep strayed.

They ran to their bikes and hurtled down the track towards the village, stopping only to collect Tim's prize trout from the bank by the stream.

Jack and Betty were woken by the tap of Tim's fishing rod on the bedroom window. The dogs barked furiously, and Jack leant out.

'What are you two doing there?' he demanded angrily.

'Dad, come quickly, we've had some sheep stolen from Marleycombe!'

'And they've taken Lop Ear.'

'We couldn't do anything about it, they were just loading them up . . . ' The children both talked at once while their parents ran downstairs.

Betty unbolted the kitchen door and let in a shivering Polly and Tim, still clutching their fishing things. But there was no time to ask more questions. Jack had already telephoned the police and he was hastily pulling on a coat over his pyjamas.

'Let's have some hot chocolate in a flask,' he said. 'The police are going to meet me up there and they want the children to come.'

At the top of Marleycombe they found that the sheep left in the field were bunched up near the gate. Some ewes were calling distractedly for their lambs, which must have been taken in the rustlers' truck.

Polly and Tim snuggled up against the dogs, wrapped in blankets and sipping their hot drinks.

At last the flashing blue light of a police car appeared in the track and Mr Fairweather arrived a few minutes later.

They all walked across the field while Polly and Tim described everything that they had seen and heard.

'I'll know better in the morning when I've had a proper count, but I reckon about twenty-five to thirty ewes and

forty or so lambs have been stolen,' said Jack. One of the police constables was making notes.

They shone their torches on the ground and paced out the distance between the gate and the spot where the truck had been parked, looking for tell-tale skid marks on the dewy grass. Jack picked up a few chips of blue paintwork that did not belong to any vehicle on the farm.

News of the rustling at Sheepfold Farm spread fast in Chalkbourne.

'Tell Brenda we think we know where her dog is,' said Polly to Walt, when he met the children buying ice creams in the village shop next morning. Betty had said they need not go to school that day, after such a late night.

'Well I'm blowed,' said Walt when Polly had described the rustler with the dog called Fly. 'Brenda's been real cut up about losing him. Better not raise her hopes too much, though. Sheepdog names are common enough . . . '

And with no new clues as to the whereabouts of the ewes and lambs, the locals soon forgot the sheep rustlers in the busy weeks of harvest which followed.

'Those orphan lambs of yours will have to go,' said Betty in exasperation at the beginning of the summer holidays. There were cries of protest from Polly and Tim. Several months ago the children had brought Blackie and Crystal back from the lambing site as tiny lambs. But now they had grown into sturdy young animals who were experts at escaping from their enclosure in the garden and eating Betty's flowers and vegetables.

'We'll take them out to graze every day of the holidays, Mum, we promise,' said Tim.

They took the lambs for walks along the farm tracks and let them nibble the grasses and herbs which grew on the verges, and which are especially tasty to sheep.

The harvest was in full swing now. Combine harvesters roared backwards and forwards in the fields of ripened corn and loaded grain lorries swished along the narrow lanes.

'I'm taking some lambs to the Chalkhill Bishop August fair. Do you want to come with me?' Jack asked Polly, Tim and Betty one day.

In late summer and early autumn, sheep fairs were held throughout the country. This was the time when flock owners and their shepherds bought and sold lambs, ewes and rams. 'Store lambs' sold at fairs were not yet ready for slaughter, and were bought to be fattened on other farms through the autumn and winter. 'Breeding ewes' and ewe lambs were bought by farmers to replace ewes they had sold, or that had died during the year. Rams were also bought for the start of the new breeding season.

Farmers and shepherds from all over the countryside gathered to discuss each other's flocks, the price of sheep, where to buy a good working collie and whether their harvest had been a good one.

Early on the morning of the Chalkhill Bishop fair, a big lorry drew up at Field Barn to collect the two hundred and fifty store lambs that Jack intended to sell. The Evans family travelled with them to count them out of the lorry at the other end and to make sure they went into pens of fifty.

By half past eight, the fair was a mass of people pouring up and down the corridors between the sheep-pens. Farmers and shepherds leant on the wattle hurdles that separated the pens studying their sale catalogues. They examined the ewes by prodding their backs, looking in their mouths and checking their udders.

Double-decker lorries came and went, spilling out their baaing passengers. Hot and bothered shepherds drove the sheep to their alloted pens.

At nine o'clock a handbell was rung and selling began. The lambs from Sheepfold Farm were not due to be sold until midday. Polly and Tim were glad their pen was in the shade of a big Sycamore tree, so the lambs would not be too hot. The children stayed with Jack and Betty, moving from pen to pen as the auctioneer rattled through the bidding at top speed.

Jack listened carefully and jotted down selling prices in his catalogue so that he could report back to Mr Fairweather after the sale. At the next fair he would replace his twenty-five stolen ewes, as well as two hundred old ewes which he planned to sell.

'And here we have lot number eleven – fifty Scotch Half-bred ewes from a well-known local vendor, Mr Goodfellow. Sound stock off local chalk downland – who'll bid me thirty pounds a ewe . . . ? Twenty-five pounds . . . ? Twenty-two pounds . . . Thank you sir, twenty-two pounds fifty . . . Twenty three pounds?'

Polly and Tim were swept along in the crowd and soon lost
their mum and dad.

'Now we move along to lot fifty – hurry along ladies and
gentlemen please, we've got a great number of sheep to get
through. Here we have twenty-five Grey-face ewes – mixed
ages – from a new vendor. First time we've sold for you, Mr
Bradley?'

Polly dug Tim hard in the ribs. 'Look!' she hissed in his
ear. 'Do you see what I see?' Tim followed the direction of
her gaze and saw, standing right next to the auctioneer, a
weasel-faced man with a gold ring in his left ear.

'Polly! It's that rustler – and just look who's in his pen!'
Polly gasped as she recognised Lop Ear.

'Thirty-five pounds I'm bid, any more offers? Thirty-five
each for a pen of twenty-five . . . '

Weasel-face melted into the crowd. With a bit of pushing
and shoving and getting some very cross looks on the way,
Polly and Tim managed to keep him in sight until he van-
ished into a refreshment tent.

'I'll wait by the entrance,' said Tim. 'You go and get Mum and Dad.'

Polly struggled back through the crush of people around the pens, until at last she saw Betty and Jack.

As soon as they heard Polly's account of how she and Tim had spotted one of the rustlers, Betty and Jack lost no time. They found two policemen on traffic duty outside the fair. Luckily one of them had been to Sheepfold Farm on the night of the rustling, so he knew all the details.

'Quickly Polly,' said Betty. 'Show us which tent the rustler is in.'

The show ground was a large one, with many tents, and Polly got rather lost.

The two policemen were just beginning to look at her impatiently when she saw Tim, still standing where she had left him.

'Take the children in with you and have a drink,' said one of the policemen. 'When you're sure he's still there, send Polly or Tim out to us. We'll come in and have a little chat to him.' He winked and grinned at Jack.

They entered the gloom of the tent and sat down nervously at a table.

Betty and Jack went to the bar for drinks and crisps, and by the time they returned Polly and Tim had seen the man. He was with two friends, hunched over beers in a dark corner. Tim was sure they must be the other rustlers.

'Finish your drinks and act as though you haven't seen him,' said Betty.

But Weasel-face had caught Polly's eye and shifted uneasily in his seat.

He muttered something to his mates and to Polly and Tim's dismay, they got up and slunk away through an open back flap in the tent.

'Now we've had it!' said Jack, leaping up. And he dashed after them, knocking over several crates of empty bottles outside.

Hearing the crash, the two policemen were just in time to see the rustlers taking to their heels. They blew their whistles, auctioneers rang their handbells and sheep in nearby pens baaed in alarm.

The rustlers ran through tents selling farm clothing and equipment, scattering goods everywhere.

At last a tea lady cornered one under an over-turned tray of doughnuts.

Another was caught up on the horns of an angry Jacob ram as he scrambled over its pen.

Weasel-face was about to sprint through one of the exits to the car park, when Jack tripped him up neatly with his crook.

Reluctantly, the thieves led the police to their battered Land Rover, where Polly and Tim found Fly and the rustlers' other dogs snarling in the back.

Brenda Roberts, who had been selling ewes at the fair, heard an announcement made about the stolen sheep and came over to claim Fly. She was horrified at how thin and nervous he had become.

Later, at Chalkhill Bishop Police Station, the chips of paint which Jack had picked up in the field were matched with scratch marks on the Land Rover's bonnet.

The thieves admitted that they had sold the stolen lambs immediately for meat, but that they had hoped to make more money by selling the ewes at the fair as breeding sheep.

Back at the farm the twenty-five stolen ewes were un-loaded from a lorry.

'Those rustlers were really daft to put you in a pen of sheep for sale,' said Polly, giving her favourite ewe a hug.

'Good old Lop Ear, we'd know you anywhere,' said Tim. 'Welcome home to Sheepfold Farm.'

Part three

Winter Comes to Sheepfold Farm

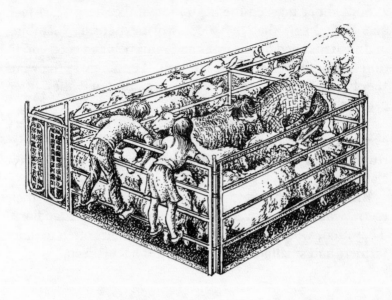

The last of the summer's corn crops had been gathered in. All over Chalkbourne Downs hedgerows were laden with ripening blackberries, elderberries and sloes.

Up at Field Barn, Polly and Tim were hanging over a gate, watching their father, Jack Evans, the shepherd at Sheepfold Farm, and Walt Roberts, the tractor driver, as they sorted out and prepared Jack's flock for the new breeding season.

September marked the beginning of the sheep year. Jack and Walt knew that the success of next spring's lambing mainly depended on the ewes and rams being in good condition at tupping time in the autumn. Tupping was the word shepherds used to describe sheep mating and they often called their rams tups.

Walt and Jack sweated in the warm sun, turning up every ewe to examine her teeth, udder and feet. Ewes with udder trouble were not kept for further breeding, and were sold for slaughter.

Broken mouth ewes, who were beginning to lose their teeth, would not do well next lambing in such a large flock. They, too, would be sold at the autumn fairs often to dairy farmers and smallholders wanting just a few sheep.

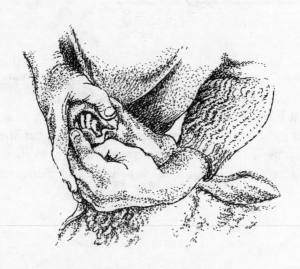

Walt and Jack cut away any overgrown or diseased parts of the ewes' hooves with clippers and then ran them through a footbath of disinfectant.

On the way home for tea, Jack, Walt, Polly and Tim stopped to feed the fifty rams of the Sheepfold Farm flock. At the beginning of August, Jack had sorted through the rams, marking any that were to be sold with the culled ewes in September. Since then, he had been feeding extra barley and oats to the others so that they would be fit and active for mating with the ewes.

The feeding plan that Jack followed for his ewes was slightly different. Once the last of the lambs had been weaned he kept the ewes on short grazing for the rest of the summer, letting the over-fat ones scavenge on the sparse

stubble fields. Then, about three weeks before tupping, he put all the ewes on to good grass and allowed them to eat well. This was called flushing.

'Why do sheep always lamb in the Spring?' asked Polly, as they watched the rams jostling for places at the feed troughs. She had never really thought about it before, but knew that horses, cows and pigs gave birth to their young at any time of year.

'It all starts with the shortening daylight hours after mid-summer,' explained Jack. 'These act as a trigger and bring ewes of most breeds into season from August to the middle of December. The ewes can only be mated with the rams when they are in season, and it takes five months for the lambs to grow inside them from the time that they are conceived. So a ewe that is tupped in October will give birth to lambs in February or March.'

A few days later, Polly and Tim were walking slowly across an old sheep pasture, searching for pink-gilled mushrooms that were beginning to grow in the fields.

Dark plumes of smoke and tongues of flame rose into the clear sky from burning stubble fields around. It was the end of harvest and most farmers were burning their unwanted straw and stubble. The fire cleaned and fertilised the soil, before the next crop was planted.

The children had half filled their baskets with mushrooms, when they reached a track running along the boundary of Sheepfold Farm.

The stubble fires were burning fiercely in a neighbouring farmer's field and both children hesitated as sudden gusts of wind blew smoke and flames in front of them, scorching trees and hedges.

They looked at some of Jack's over-fat ewes grazing peacefully across the track from the burning fields. Suddenly a wisp of loose burning straw was caught up into a whirlwind of hot air, carried a few yards and then dropped down on to the unburned stubble of the Sheepfold Farm field.

In a minute, a ripple of tiny flames sprang up.

There was no time to be lost. Polly and Tim knew how fast fire spread in dry straw; already it was too late to stamp it out.

'Quick Polly! We must get the sheep out of here! Go and open the gate in the far corner,' shouted Tim. Luckily, the stubble was surrounded by grass fields which would not catch fire.

By now the flock had scented danger and were beginning to run in a blind panic. Tim tried vainly to gather them. If only he had one of his father's dogs, Floss, Tib or Patch. His eyes began to stream but he could just make out the open

gateway and Polly running back around the sheep. Through the clouds of smoke, he glimpsed a lithe black and white shape streaking across the field.

'FLOSS! 'Way to me!' he yelled above the crackling roar of the flames. But the dog did not respond to the usual commands and began to make odd darting movements into the sheep, scattering them, instead of circling the flock. In desperation, Tim picked a blade of grass and, cupping his hands, whistled loudly on it.

The dog paused and then ran swiftly round the flock towards the sound. It was just enough to get the sheep moving in the direction of the gateway. Soon they were pouring into the grass field, flanked on either side by Polly, Tim and the dog – minutes before the fire caught them up.

The children ran a little way into the cool moist grass and flung themselves down.

When they looked up, the fire was nearly out, leaving a blackened smouldering field.

There was no sign of the dog anywhere.

———

'That's Higgins not ploughing a wide enough strip round his stubble. He always was careless,' said Jack angrily, when Polly and Tim found him in the farmyard. 'I'd better get up there double quick and make sure the fire is really out.'

'It couldn't have been Floss or any of the dogs. They were shut up in their kennels here at home,' said Betty, their mother, when she heard about the rescue of the sheep. But no one could shed any light on where the mystery dog came from.

———

Next day was the start of the autumn term. Polly and Tim set off for school, feeling hot and itchy in their new winter uniforms, gloomily thinking of the freedom and excitement of the summer holidays that were now over.

However, they were slightly cheered by the thought of a day at Chalkhill Bishop Great Fair the following week. Jack would be selling his culled sheep and buying in some new tups and breeding ewes for the flock, and Polly, Tim and Betty were going with him.

All over the country, in preparation for the autumn fairs, ram breeders were busy washing and clipping their rams' fleeces. It was skilful work, intended to emphasise the rams' deep chests and long, broad backs. Walt called it scornfully 'an optical delusion'.

On the morning of the Chalkhill Bishop Fair the well-groomed rams arrived in a variety of vehicles – some even in the back seats of cars.

Jack unloaded his ewes and rams from a lorry and, after driving them to their pens, he met up with his boss, Mr Fairweather. They went round the pens of rams and ewes, carefully noting down in their sale catalogues the ones they were interested in buying.

Polly, Tim and Betty enjoyed looking round at the more unusual breeds of rams, which had enthusiastic owners hovering over them.

Polly thought the long crinkly fleece of a Wensleydale ram was beautiful, and wished Mr Fairweather would buy him for the Sheepfold Farm flock.

Dorset and Hampshire Down, and Suffolk rams were the most popular breeds in the area. Ewes that were mated with these rams gave birth to sturdy, fast-growing lambs.

The Hampshire and Dorset Down were stocky sheep, with broad, well fleshed rumps and brown ears and faces, framed by clumps of wool on their cheeks and foreheads.

The Suffolk was renowned for its long back, and fine glossy black head and legs.

Polly and Tim watched nervous breeders tap their prize rams around a ring to show them off at their best to prospective buyers.

'They are handsome creatures – no doubt about that,' said Betty to Jack, gasping at the high prices some of the rams were fetching.

There was a bit of fighting when the rams bought at the fair were introduced to those already at the farm. Jack penned them up together for a few days to allow them to make friends. Walt made hay collars for the new rams to encourage the others to nuzzle them and so become used to their smell.

Some new ewe lambs arrived by lorry from the North as replacements for ewes sold at the fair, and Jack and Walt were kept busy all the following week, preparing them for tupping.

They were vaccinated to prevent them bringing any serious diseases to the flock and to give immunity to the lambs they would have in the future.

Then Jack round-tailed the ewe lambs by shearing the wool away from their tails and hindquarters. This made it easier for the rams to mate with them properly.

Finally they were 'drenched' with a special medicine, which killed all the worms in their digestive tracts, and flushed on fresh pasture.

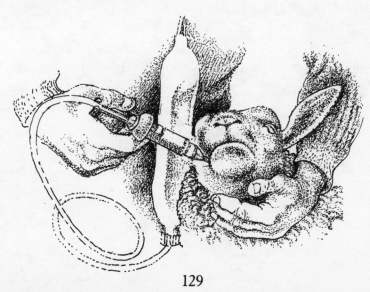

Next weekend, Polly and Tim gave Jack a hand cleaning the ram harnesses. At tupping time, each ram wore one of these so that, when he mated with a ewe, he left a coloured mark on her rump from a special colour block called a crayon, fixed to the breast strap.

'Which colour will you use first, Dad?' asked Tim, as they worked away, saddle-soaping the stiff, mildewed leather.

'Blue for the early lambing flock, then red, then green for the April lambing lot,' said Jack, tapping the old worn crayons from their holders with a hammer.

Jack and Walt had divided the fifteen hundred ewes at Sheepfold Farm into three flocks. The six hundred in best condition would go to the ram at the end of September. The rams would be put out wearing blue crayons in their harnesses and all those ewes marked blue at the end of two or three weeks made up the early flock, to begin lambing at the end of February.

Each flock of ewes would have been with teaser rams about two weeks before tupping began. Teasers were rams made infertile by an operation. Their presence stimulated the ewes to come into season so that when the fertile rams went out with them, they were tupped very quickly.

'What's so special about today?' said Polly as she and Tim scrambled for their schoolbags one morning towards the end of September. The sheep calendar hanging in the kitchen was marked with a big red circle around the twenty-seventh.

'Have you forgotten?' laughed Betty. 'This is the day the rams go out with the early flock!'

Polly and Tim left the shepherd's cottage in good time for school and ran up the lane.

They could see Jack and Walt ahead of them, unloading rams from the Land Rover and trailer, which were parked by the gateway to a field called Toby's Bottom. Jack had split the ewes into two lots of three hundred and since one mature ram would tup up to forty or fifty ewes, he was putting ten rams in with each flock.

The rams lumbered down the ramp of the trailer. A group of ewes detached themselves from the rest of the flock and went forward to meet them.

'It looks as though the teasers have done their job,' said Walt.

When the ewes were in season and ready to mate, their smell attracted the rams. A ewe and a ram would become especially interested in each other and circle round, nuzzling and talking. The ewe would allow the ram to jump up and straddle her back with his forelegs, so that his chest was resting on her rump. In this position, he could successfully mate with her.

'The rams are working well – time to change the colour crayon and to put more rams out with the next lot of ewes,' said Jack to Betty several weeks later, when he counted five hundred blue-bottomed ewes. That was a big enough flock to fill the lambing site at Field Barn.

The kitchen of the shepherd's cottage was fragrant with the smells of fruit pies and bubbling saucepans of jam and chutney. Betty was preparing food for the harvest supper to be held in the village hall.

Everyone looked forward to this annual feast, and this year it turned out to be as much fun as ever. The three Sheepfold Farm tractor drivers, Walt, Bob White and Bert Penny, got quite merry on the cider and there were lots of speeches and songs, and ragging between the arable workers, cowmen and shepherds.

Jack and the other shepherds compared prices they had obtained for their fat lambs and swopped stories about the lambing season and the summer's sheep rustling.

Brenda Roberts, Walt's niece who was shepherdess at Blagdon Farm, offered Jack some autumn 'keep' for his ewes; two crops of stubble turnips that her own flock did not need.

The days grew shorter and a nip of autumn was in the air. Jack bought himself a new winter hat.

One weekend, Polly and Tim were collecting conkers from the big old horse chestnut tree in the farmyard, when the shepherd's van drew up with a jerk and Jack got out. Polly and Tim could tell he was in a rage and scurried after him, asking what the matter was.

'It's those ewes in Toby's Bottom – found 'em in a terrible state this morning, driven against the fence and as jittery as frightened cats,' he told them later over a cup of coffee.

Betty stroked Beulah their grey cat, who was tightly curled up in her lap. 'It couldn't be rustlers again, could it – have you counted the ewes?'

'No, a dog has had a go at them,' said Jack. 'There are several with torn fleeces and nips on their flanks. This'll cost us a few lambs.'

The first weeks of a ewe's pregnancy were a risky time for the developing lamb embryos. The mother could easily lose her lambs if she was roughly handled or frightened.

Jack borrowed Mr Fairweather's gun and stayed down in Toby's Bottom a few nights, hoping to catch the culprit. Farmers were entitled to shoot dogs they caught worrying their livestock.

But whatever it was that had stirred up the sheep, did not return.

Towards the end of October, Jack had a phone call from Brenda Roberts to say that the stubble turnips were ready.

Jack wanted to keep his crops of kale and swedes in reserve for as long as possible. But he would soon have to think about giving the ewes extra food, because the late autumn grass no longer contained enough nourishment for them and their developing lambs. So he was glad of Brenda's offer.

'We'll walk the early flock along the old ox drove tomorrow,' he said to Walt. 'Since it's half term, maybe Polly, Tim and Betty will help.'

Early in the morning, the dogs gathered the blue flock and twelve rams from a field near the drove and they set off at a gentle pace towards Blagdon Farm.

'Steady there!' roared Jack at the dogs every now and then, worried that they were driving the pregnant ewes too hard.

Among the blue flock was Lop Ear, Polly and Tim's favourite ewe who had been stolen by rustlers in the summer. The children were sorry that Lop Ear had not yet been marked by a ram. Any ewe who was not pregnant by the end of tupping time was called a barrener and usually sent to market in the Spring, unless she was a young one.

'This puts me in mind of when I was a boy,' said Walt as they settled down to have a snack half way between Sheep-fold Farm and Blagdon.

The sheep grazed at the edges of the drove under the watchful eyes of the dogs.

'Did you help with the sheep in those days?' asked Betty.

'My old dad was shepherd for the Watsons – just over the ridge there – and we used to drive the sheep to Chalkhill Bishop Fairs along this drove. Folks have used it for hundreds of years to drive cattle and sheep to market. It used to be kept trimmed right back. Now look how over-grown it is.'

Polly wondered how shepherds going to the fair stopped their different flocks mixing up.

'Well, in them days we had the Old English sheepdogs – there weren't the collies about then, y'know,' explained Walt, 'and although they was such great hairy things, they could work. We relied on them to keep the flocks apart.'

They came down off the drove at Blagdon and Brenda directed them to one of her spare fields of stubble turnips.

The sheep would be put on to a narrow strip (or fold) of turnips and allowed to eat from morning until nightfall. Then Brenda's dog, Fly, would bring them back on to an adjoining grass field for the night.

When they had completely eaten the turnips in the netted piece, Brenda would take up the dividing fence and let them into a fresh fold. So they would move across the whole field, grazing each piece thoroughly until the whole crop was eaten off.

Jack reckoned the two fields would last about eight weeks. 'We'll bring 'em back just before Christmas,' he said.

For the rest of the half term holiday, Polly and Tim got up early each day, to check round the sheep with Jack. On Friday morning, they stopped at Pug's Hole, where three hundred of the red flock were grazing, and peered through the thick autumnal mist. There was no sign of the ewes or the rams. Polly picked up handfuls of wool, scattered over the frosty grass.

'As I expected,' said Jack grimly, when they found a ewe badly tangled in a wire fence and the rest of the flock huddled together in a nervous heap. 'Sheep worriers again.'

'We must get to the bottom of this – I'll stay up there tonight with my gun,' said Mr Fairweather, when Jack told him what had happened.

That evening was Hallowe'en and Polly and Tim planned to go tricking or treating round the village with their friends.

Someone had given them two big pumpkins and they scooped out the pulp and cut grinning faces in the shells.

As soon as darkness fell, Rosie and George Hawkins and a gang of others came knocking at the shepherd's cottage door. Polly and Tim were just fixing night lights into the pumpkin lanterns.

Floss, Tib and Patch growled from their kennels in the yard at the weird crew clustered round the doorstep and at the witch and ghost who swept out to join them.

'Back by eight-thirty, mind!' Betty shouted after the golden globes of light bobbing down the lane.

They rapped on window panes and made spooky noises through letterboxes. Most people chose to give a treat, such as an orange or an apple and a mug of something hot, rather than risk being booby trapped.

Their last stop on the way home was at a newly renovated cottage called *The Nook*.

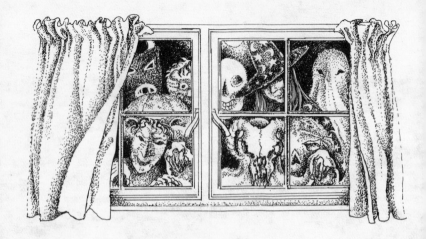

'Waah!' wailed Rosie Hawkins through the letterbox and the door was opened cautiously. A woman with a plump, kind face peered out at them. When she saw their homemade disguises and the pumpkin lanterns, she gave them an uncertain smile.

'You gave us a scare with that horrible racket – we'd got to expect fireworks and the like being pushed through our door in the town. You'd better come in – what is it you're after?'

They trooped through the warm lighted hall into a comfortable, chintzy living room where the woman's husband and a collie were watching sheepdog trials on television. The dog followed the flickering pictures of sheep on the screen and whined excitedly, ears erect, after every command and whistle.

The programme was just ending and the woman's husband reluctantly turned the television off.

They chatted about the village and surrounding farms and ate Mrs Bailey's tasty shortbread. Mr and Mrs Bailey were newcomers to Chalkbourne. They told the children how they had moved from the town when they had retired.

'Thought it would be lovely, but we're finding it hard to make friends,' sighed Mrs Bailey.

'That's why we got Jess,' said Mr Bailey, toeing the silky flank at his feet. 'We've always loved border collies since we've seen them working on that telly programme – wonderful dogs.'

'My Dad says collies kept as pets are a proper nuisance,' said Rosie Hawkins.

'Now and then she strays off when we let her out at night,' went on Mrs Bailey, not noticing Rosie's disapproval. 'Yesterday evening she didn't come back till the small hours.'

Tim caught Polly's eye. Could it be Jess who was worrying the Sheepfold Farm sheep?

Polly shivered and thought of Mr Fairweather, lying in wait up at Pug's Hole with his gun. Jess lay stretched out on the hearthrug, looking as though butter wouldn't melt in her mouth.

Much later than half past eight, Polly and Tim hurried back along the lane to Sheepfold Farm. As they rounded the last bend, a dark shape overtook them on the other side of the hedge.

Both children started nervously. They remembered a story told by Walt of a shepherd and his dog who had frozen to death in a snowstorm in Pug's Hole many years ago. But somehow that shape was familiar . . .

'Jess!' cried Polly in dismay. 'Come on Tim, we've got to stop Mr Fairweather shooting her!'

They found Mr Fairweather hiding in a clump of gorse overlooking the sheep who were camped in hollows about the field.

Polly and Tim barely had time to tell him about Jess, before she appeared out of the hedge line. In a trice she was

causing panic among the sleeping sheep. Leaping and snapping, she ran this way and that, until finally she singled out one ewe and chased her relentlessly up and down the field.

'Let us try to call her, we know the owners, they'll be terribly upset if you shoot her,' pleaded Polly.

'I'll give you one chance to call her off. Be quick – before she pulls the ewe down,' said Mr Fairweather, his hand on his gun.

'Jessie! Heel!' called Tim urgently.

But the dog took no notice.

Tim picked a blade of grass and whistled with all his might.

Jess stopped dead in her tracks. Polly and Tim ran down the field calling her all the time. She began to trot towards them, wagging her tail.

Mrs and Mrs Bailey were very relieved to have Jess back and shocked to hear about the sheep worrying. By now, Polly and Tim were sure she was the mysterious dog who had helped push the ewes out of the burning field. They described the fierce stubble fire and how Jess had not responded to Tim's commands until he whistled on a blade of grass.

'She might have been a good working dog if she'd been trained as a pup,' said Mr Fairweather gruffly, 'but if I ever catch her worrying my sheep again – I won't give her a second chance.'

———

The second half of the autumn term was tidying up time on the farm. Most of the stubble fields had been ploughed up and the winter corn planted. The last fields to be ploughed would be left unsown until March when the spring corn would be put in.

Jack and Walt repaired broken sheep-fences and dipped all the wattle hurdles in creosote (a preservative) ready for next lambing.

Walt, Bert and Bob trimmed back hedgerows, cut down dead trees and lit huge brushwood bonfires in the fields. On November the fifth, Jack changed the colour in the rams' harnesses from red to green and put more rams out with the last five hundred ewes.

Polly, Tim and Rosie Hawkins and her gang often called in to see Mr and Mrs Bailey in the dark autumn days following Hallowe'en.

Polly and Tim took Jess out for extra walks, taking care to have her on a lead when near cattle and sheep. They practised getting the Baileys' chickens in at night with her. She was quick to learn and becoming very obedient.

The winter days grew shorter and soon it was December.

Mrs White stocked the village shop with Christmas goodies and hung the window with tinsel and paper chains.

Chalkbourne school hummed with excitement and the children began to rehearse their Christmas nativity play. Polly and Tim were to be two of the three shepherds, but they were horrified at the fluffy toy lamb Miss Jenkins wanted them to carry.

'It doesn't look anything like a real lamb,' grumbled Polly, 'if only we had some on the farm . . . '

'Brenda's phoned to say the blues have nearly finished the stubble turnips at Blagdon,' said Betty to Jack, one Friday afternoon near the end of term.

'We'll walk them back on Sunday – they were looking pretty fit when I saw them last week,' said Jack.

On Sunday afternoon, Walt dropped the Evans family off at Blagdon Farm and they all walked up to the stubble turnips where they met Brenda. They thanked her for looking after the Sheepfold Farm sheep and Jack whistled to his dogs to bring the flock out of the field.

'Happy Christmas!' shouted Polly and Tim, looking back and waving as they walked behind the sheep, along a track up to the drove.

150

Holly trees bright with scarlet berries, and dark yews, leaned over the old green road. Polly and Tim broke off boughs to take home for Christmas decorations.

They were about three quarters of the way back to Sheep-fold Farm, and the light was fading fast, when Polly and Tim noticed Lop Ear dropping behind the rest of the flock. Finally she refused to be driven any further and turned on the dogs, butting them angrily.

'What's the matter with her, Mum, is she ill?' Polly asked Betty.

Betty walked over to where Lop Ear stood, with sides heaving and head down.

'Good heavens! She's lambing!' she said after a few minutes.

They were all worried at first that the lambs would be tiny premature things. But Lop Ear gave birth to a fine healthy pair of twins, very white with little horn stubs showing on their heads.

Jack looked puzzled. 'Full term lambs all right – where did you get 'em from my girl? No Dorset Down or Suffolk ram fathered these!' he said.

'She must have been tupped in July,' said Betty 'no wonder our rams didn't mark her.'

'Maybe she got with a ram when the rustlers had her – a Dorset Horn by the looks of those lambs,' said Jack.

'We should have noticed that she was bagged up,' said Betty. About two or three weeks before lambing, a pregnant ewe's udder would become much larger as it filled with milk.

It was nightfall by the time the early lambing flock reached Sheepfold Farm.

Bringing up the rear, came Polly and Tim, each carrying a newborn lamb, and closely followed by Lop Ear.

Polly and Tim came home from school on Monday, cross and tired after the final dress rehearsal in the village church.

Polly had persuaded Miss Jenkins to let them bring one of Lop Ear's beautiful lambs as the shepherds' gift to Jesus. But the lamb bawled loudly, drowning the infants' carol, while Polly, Tim and Dan Stewart processed up the aisle to the chancel steps.

Then it wriggled free from Tim's arms as they were kneeling at the manger and ran off, nuzzling everybody's legs in search of milk.

'The thing to do,' said Jack when he heard about these disasters, 'is to tuck a bottle of Lop Ear's milk into your shepherd's pouch and give the lamb a good feed whenever it gets restless.'

Tuesday was the night of the nativity play and after school Polly and Tim ran down the lane to the village to ask Mr and Mrs Bailey to come.

The sky was studded with brilliant stars and little decorated Christmas trees winked and glittered in the cottage windows of Chalkbourne.

Before going indoors, Polly and Tim went to see Lop Ear and her lambs, snug in a wattle hurdle pen with a roof which Jack had made for her in the garden.

Lop Ear stood quietly while Tim squeezed some milk from her warm, full udder, into a bottle.

Polly picked up her smaller lamb. 'It's all right girl, we'll bring him back soon,' she said.

All Chalkbourne school assembled in the church vestry, where some volunteer mums helped them to dress in their costumes. The infants peeped through the vestry curtains to wave at the audience gathering in the nave.

Garlands of holly and ivy tumbled from every pillar and window-ledge; candles shimmered in the choir stalls. Polly and Tim thought they had never seen the church look so beautiful.

Gradually a hush fell on the chattering audience as all but a few lights were turned out and the low sweet tones of 'Once in Royal David's City' filled the old stone building.

The juniors sang like angels and the infants remembered nearly all their words.

The three kings strode up the aisle in their royal robes, drawing murmurs of admiration from the audience.

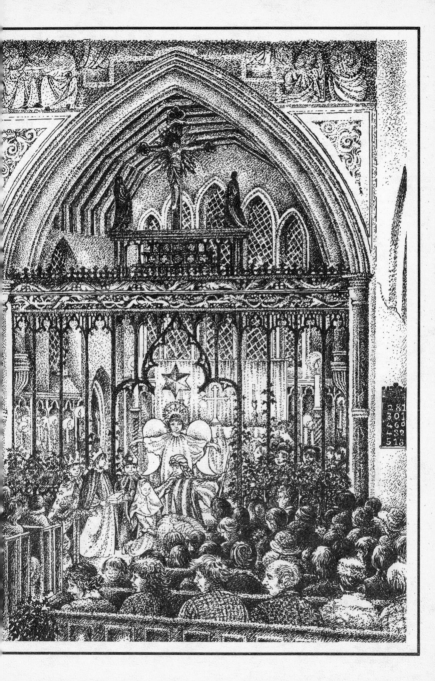

The shepherds walked slowly and humbly to the manger with Polly playing 'Oh Leave Your Sheep' on her recorder, while Tim carried Lop Ear's lamb, nestling drowsily in his arms.

Jack and Betty thought about their flocks sleeping on the Downs and of the busy lambing season to come.

'We wish you a Merry Christmas,
And a Happy New Year . . .'

sang Mary, Joseph, angels, kings, shepherds and all the children of Chalkbourne school, grinning broadly at the prospect of the glorious holidays ahead.